You Are More Than What You Weigh

WORKBOOK

IMPROVE YOUR SELF-ESTEEM
NO MATTER WHAT YOUR WEIGHT

Sharon Norfleet Sward, LPC

YOU ARE MORE THAN
WHAT YOU WEIGH WORKBOOK

Improve Your Self-esteem No Matter What Your Weight

By Sharon Sward

Published by:
Wholesome Publisher
1231 S. Parker Rd. #102
Denver, CO 80231

Library of Congress Cataloging-in-Publication Data
Sward, Sharon
  You are more than what you weigh: improve your self-esteem no
  matter what your weight / Sharon Norfleet Sward. --2nd ed.
  p. cm.
  ISBN: 0-9648874-3-6

  1. Eating disorders--Psychological aspects. 2. Body image 3. Obesity--
     Psychological aspects. 4. Self-esteem.   I. Title

  BF697.5.B63S93 1998   616.85'26
                                          QBI97-40894
  95-61855
                    CIP

I N T R O D U C T I O N

Why This Book is for You

*Y*ou Are More Than What You Weigh Workbook *is an accompaniment to* You Are More Than What You Weigh. *You Are More Than What You Weigh* gives you the background to be able to complete the exercises in the workbook. If you prefer to work on your computer, CD or disks are also available. (See the back page on instructions of how to obtain them.) Both of these books are about improving your self-image. You do not have to be at your ideal weight in order to love yourself and your body. If you have tried to lose weight and haven't succeeded in keeping it off, this book will help you understand the reasons behind your weight problems. It will give you the tools to help you make the changes you desire. If you are ambivalent about changing your eating habits and weight, you can benefit by changing your thoughts instead. Whether you are at your ideal weight, underweight, overweight, or purging, this book will aid you in becoming healthier. More significantly, it will help you love yourself no matter what you weigh. This is about you…the most important person. You are valuable, lovable, and worthwhile. Even if you find it inconceivable now, you will believe it by the time you read and work through the exercises in *You Are More Than What You Weigh Workbook.*

How This Book Can Help You

Unfortunately, society has conditioned us to think that thinner is better. One of the reasons you may have set yourself up for failure in the past is that you might have tied your identity only to your weight. Besides your weight or physical self, you want to value and identify yourself with the other aspects of yourself. These other aspects include the following ten types of selves:

■■■

iii

You Are More Than What You Weigh

1. **Physical Self** *(weight and body image)*
2. **Intellectual Self** *(your thoughts)*
3. **Emotional Self** *(your feelings)*
4. **Social Self** *(your relationships)*
5. **Psychological Self** *(identity and self-esteem)*
6. **Spiritual Self** *(higher power and values)*
7. **Sexual Self** *(male and female traits)*
8. **Assertive Self** *(express feelings to others)*
9. **Stress/Relaxed Self** *(stress causes and remedies)*
10. **Career Self** *(career analysis)*

How these ten parts of yourself influence your weight, body image, eating, and self-esteem are explored in this workbook. For example, compare yourself to a circle with ten equal parts. Your physical being is one piece of the circle along with the other nine parts. When all ten parts of yourself are equally important, you and your live are balanced. You are not a well-rounded person when your physical self is the only important part of you. You are free to experience life in a new way when you are not consumed with your weight.

If you do not know how to journal, this workbook will teach you how. You may choose to journal whatever you feel or think daily, or only when needed. You may want to journal by answering the exercises in this workbook. For example, on page 4, # 3 exercise:

Journal your feelings and thoughts related to your body fat. Underline with different colored pens each instance that you write negative or positive thoughts about your body fat.

If you already have a journal, you can underline the negative and positive statements you make about your body. You may, however, wish to write your feelings and thoughts about your body and fat. Begin your journal by doing the exercises that are pertinent to you. You do not have to do them in any particular order. You may choose to work on the exercises alone, with a friend, or in a group. On the charts in this workbook, you will notice (1-10) after many of the topics. (1=feels terrible 10=feels terrific) This will help you to be aware of your thinking and feelings. You will empower yourself when you determine the action you need to take to make the changes you desire.

Remember that life is a process. It has taken many years to develop your present patterns of behavior. Each day is a new day for you to change and to enjoy these changes. I wish you well in your journey to make your dreams come true and for you to become more than what you weigh.

Acknowledgement

As a licensed professional counselor, I would like to thank my many clients whose experiences have helped me write this book. To my new friends on the Internet who have shared their experiences, I look forward to learning more from you. As president of Eating Disorder Professionals of Colorado, I have learned from our speakers, workshops, and professional friends. Thanks especially to Jeremy A. Lazarus, Larry Laycob, M.D., Susan Richardson, Ph.D. and Jack McInroe, Ed.D. for their supervision that helped me become the therapist I am today. My appreciation to my personal therapists, Dr. Robert Hoffman, Dr. Ralph E. Roughton and group leader Pat Penelton, who helped me in my personal development. Thanks also to Jill Mordini, Dr. Cheryl Arnold, Rosy Hughes, Kim Johansen, Pat Patterson, Amy Mauro and Ruth Astuno for their suggestions. I also want to thank my special friends now and in my past. I have had many great teachers, both in and out of the classroom, which have taught me about life and myself. Last, but not least, thanks to my parents Myrtle and Leland Norfleet, my Aunt Madeline, my brothers Ken, Jerry, Jim, and John and my sister Karen. Thanks also to my husband Larry and two children, Brian and Melinda, for their patience during the writing of this book and continually teach me about being a parent and a wife.

Table of Contents

Tables and Charts

Tables and Charts

What Professionals Say About this Book

National Eating Disorder Organization
Laureate Psychiatric Clinic Hospital Eating Disorders Program

You Are More Than What You Weigh is an inspirational and upbeat text expressing how women and men of today can learn to love themselves and improve self-image regardless of weight, size or shape. With great practical insight, Ms. Sward directs readers to begin to search internally for worth, instead of turning to food and others for satisfaction and comfort surrounding personal identity.

National Association of Anorexia Nervosa & Associated Disorders
Vivian Meehan, President of ANAD

Happy to list your workbook in our bibliography since it is a worth-while and helpful book. It is organized well and we believe it would be helpful to many.

The Children's Hospital
Jennifer Hagman, Medical Director

It is nice to have your book for our patients at Children's Hospital. There is a lot of valuable information in this book for them.

Colorado and American Psychiatric Society
Jeremy A. Lazarus, M.D. Past President of CPS and Past Ethics Chair of APS

You Are More Than What You Weigh is clearly written and should benefit anyone interested in confronting the psychological barriers in weight control.

Columbia/Bethesda Eating Disorder Treatment Center-Denver
Kenneth Weiner, M.D. Medical Director at Bethesda Hospital in Denver and Owner of Treatment Center

You Are More Than What You Weigh is a practical and user friendly guide to help those with an eating disorder work on their sense of self and maximize their recovery.

The Midwest Book Review

James A. Cox, Editor in Chief

You Are More Than What You Weigh is the ideal self-help guide for anyone concerned about their weight and self esteem. *You Are More Than What You Weigh* is a compendium of sound, practical advice, counsel and exercises. HIGHLY RECOMMENDED!

Colorado Mental Health Counselors Association

Tamara Golden, President

You Are More Than What You Weigh is a valuable resource to assist clients in taking self-responsibility and giving them tools to use between counseling sessions.

Colorado Psychiatric Society

Deborah Stetler, M.D. Co-editor of the CPS and liaison to the
American Psychiatric Society Research Network

You Are More Than What You Weigh is a straightforward, no-nonsense series of written exercises to help persons with distorted eating discover other aspects of themselves (i.e., intellectual, social, spiritual).

Eating Disorder Professionals of Colorado

Richard Lindsey, Ph.D., CEAP; Past President of EDPC

You Are More Than What You Weigh approach is active, holistic and solution-focused. The book, in its presentation, is inherently hopeful, practical and helpful in a loving, forgiving and accepting way.

Clinical Nutrition Center

James Berry, M.D. Owner and President

You Are More Than What You Weigh will help you to understand your problem and how to deal with it effectively.

C H A P T E R   O N E

Accept and Love Your Body

After each body part, check whether you like or dislike that part of your body. Then indicate how this part of your body helps you. For those body parts you like, indicate what action you can take to emphasize this positive feeling. For the parts of your body, you dislike, indicate action you can take to feel more positive about your body.

BODY PART	LIKE	DISLIKE	FUNCTION OF MY BODY PART	ACTION TO TAKE
Hips				
Arms				
Stomach				
Fingers				
Buttocks				
Hair				
Breast				
Legs				
Waist				
Ears				
Nose				
Feet				
Teeth				

■■■

SELF EVALUATION:

1. Make a list of people in my life who have had a major impact on the image I have of myself. How did they shape my attitude toward myself as a child and adult?

   a. *Parents:*
   b. *Brothers-Sisters:*
   c. *Co-workers:*
   d. *Friends:*
   e. *Teachers:*
   f. *Boss:*

2. What is some positive feedback I have received about my body? Do I allow these reactions to be received or do I discount them?

3. Imagine getting rid of the voice that says eat and I will feel better. What thinking can I use to replace it?

4. If my body could talk what would it say to me?

5. What would I like to say to my body?

6. Let my body become my friend instead of my object of fear or disgust. What action can I take to make this happen?

2

7. What are my fears in having a positive relationship with my body?

8. Beliefs I can use to accept my body:

EXERCISES:

1. *Describe your experience of being a baby, child, adolescent, and adult. What changes in your body and body image have taken place at each of these times in your life? Can you pinpoint the period in your life when you began to feel negative about your body?

2. *Look at yourself in the mirror, seeing yourself as others see you. Do not judge and do not criticize yourself. Say nice things about yourself as you look into the mirror. Continue this exercise until you believe what you say.

3. *Look at or imagine your family at a reunion. How are you similar and different from others in your family? What is the weight of the males vs. females in your family?

4. Write down ten words that describe your negative feelings and attitudes about your body. Allow yourself to experience fully what it means for you to identify yourself this way. Now let go of this self-identification as if you were taking off your clothes. Replace it with a healthy image. On a scale of 1-10, how does it feel to let go of your negative attitudes toward your body? (1= feels awful; 10= feels great.)

5. Visualize yourself accepting your body today. Remember to start with one part of your body at a time. Close your eyes and get in a peaceful state of mind. Relax and begin to get in touch with your body. How does your body feel? Your head? Your shoulders? Your arms? Your breasts? Your stomach? Your legs? Your feet?

Reprinted with permission by Marcia Germaine Hutchinson. © 1985. Published by Crossing Press. Freedom, CA..

"Good bye Fat"

SELF EVALUATION:

1. Fears of letting go of my undesirable fat:

2. Advantages of letting go of my undesirable fat:

3. How can I value/treasure my healthy body fat?

4. Beliefs that would help me appreciate my healthy body fat:

EXERCISES:

1. Visualize yourself letting go of undesirable fat. On a scale of 1-10, how does it feel to no longer have your excess fat? What is a first step in making this happen? Be sure to choose a goal, which promotes success.

2. Have a dialogue with your fat. What do you need to say to your fat? What does your fat need to say to you?

3. Journal your feelings and thoughts about your body fat. Underline with different colored pens each instance that you write negative and positive statements about your body. This will allow you to chart your progress.

Fat Chart

List your excess fat's purposes. After each purpose, indicate a healthy
way to meet this need or purpose. (1= feels awful; 10= feels wonderful)

PURPOSE OF MY FAT (1-10)	ACTION TO TAKE (1-10)
Protection	
Prevents Promiscuity	
Safety from Sexual Abuse	
To be Noticed	
Power and Strength	
Other purposes	

Medical Problems

SELF EVALUATION:

1. Fears I have regarding my health:

2. Beliefs I have that are related to my health:

3. Beliefs about my health which would be helpful:

4. My eating and weight are related to my medical problems:

5. Potential benefits for use of an anti-depressant:

6. Family history of persons who were on medications for depression:

7. Action I could take instead of or in addition to an anti-depressant to fight my depression:

EXERCISES:

1. Visualize yourself not having the medical problems you now have. On a scale of 1-10, how does this feel? Is there any action you can take to lessen your medical problems? What keeps you from taking this action?

2. Visualize yourself lessening your depression, urge to eat, and obsessive thoughts about food. Visualize yourself no longer bingeing or purging. How does that feel? What action do you need to take to make that happen?

Medical Chart

Make a list of your family's health problems. Indicate the severity of the problem and action you can take to not get the same problems.

MEDICAL PROBLEMS		SEVERITY (1-10)	ACTION TO TAKE (1-10)
TYPE	FAMILY'S		
Diabetes			
Hypoglycemia			
Liver			
Kidney			
Heart			
Cholesterol			
Circulation			
Elimination			
Other			

Exercise and Metabolism

SELF EVALUATION:

1. **Benefits I could get from exercising:**

2. **Excuses I give for not exercising or over exercising:**

3. **Type of exercise that I would most enjoy:**

4. **When I over exercise, it keeps me from thinking about:**

5. **My eating is related to my exercise:**

6. **Things I do that decrease the speed of my metabolism:**

EXERCISES:

1. Visualize yourself exercising in the way that is most enjoyable for you. On a scale of 1-10, how does it feel not to exercise? To exercise?

2. Write in your journal your feelings about exercising.

Exercise Diary

Keep a record of the type and amount of exercise that you do daily.
Indicate the intensity of the exercise and how you feel afterwards.

TYPE OF EXERCISE	EXERCISE AMOUNT	EXERCISE INTENSITY (1-10)	HOW EXERCISE MAKES ME FEEL (1-10)
Walk			
Run			
Swim			
Aerobic Exercises			
Biking			
Hiking			
Snow Sports			
Water Sports			
Weight Lifting			
Other			

Stop the Deprivation

SELF EVALUATION:

1. When I deprive myself, I feel:

2. My fears of not depriving myself:

3. Beliefs that I could change about depriving myself:

4. Depriving myself influences my eating:

EXERCISES:

1. Fill a plate full of food, filling it with as much as the plate can hold. Make it abundant. Now eat this food slowly. You have an abundance of food and an abundance of time. What feelings does this bring up for you?

2. Visualize yourself believing there is plenty and you no longer need to deprive yourself. On a scale of 1-10, how do you feel when you think abundance? Deprivation?

3. Write in your journal the ways you deprive yourself. Go back after writing and indicate with different colored pens when you are depriving yourself and when you are not.

Deprivation Chart

When do you deprive yourself and when do you have feelings of abundance? What action can you take to make the changes you desire?

SITUATION	DEPRIVED BEHAVIORS (1-10)	FEELINGS OF ABUNDANCE (10)	ACTION TO TAKE TO CHANGE (1-10)
Food			
Exercise			
Money			
Material Items			
Time			
Support			
Recreation			
Laughter			
Other			

Eat When Physically Hungry

SELF EVALUATION:

1. **I eat when I am physically hungry:**

2. **I eat when I am not physically hungry because:**

3. **When I eat when I am not physically hungry I feel:**

EXERCISES:

1. Visualize yourself eating when hungry and stopping when full. Practice until it becomes a habit. On a scale of 1-10, how does this feel?

2. Keep a journal of what level of hunger you are at when you eat. Also, indicate how full you are when you stop.

3. Use the physical hunger chart to measure your physical hunger before and after eating. (1=starving and 10=stuffed.)

Physical Hunger Chart

	Breakfast	Snack	Lunch	Snack	Dinner	Snack
Physical hunger before eating						
Physical hunger after eating						

Break the Destructive Habits and Addictions

SELF EVALUATION:

1. Name family members that have had a drug or alcohol problem.

2. What were the actions that family members took to overcome their addiction that I could use for my addictions?

3. Write those habits I wish to break. How long have I had the habit?

4. Where did I learn these habits? What would the people who taught me these habits think if I changed these habits?

EXERCISES:

1. Visualize yourself without drugs, alcohol or a food addiction. On a scale of 1-10, how does it feel without your addiction?

2. Visualize yourself breaking the habit that you have chosen to stop. On a scale of 1-10, how does it feel to continue the habit? Change the habit?

3. Write in your journal the habits you wish to change.

Habits Chart

List your unhealthy habits. Then choose a healthy habit to replace the unhealthy one. What action do you need to take to make these changes?

UNHEALTHY HABITS (1-10)	HEALTHY HABITS (1-10)	ACTION TO TAKE (1-10)
Alcohol		
Drugs		
Emotional Eating		
Skip Meals		
Eat Fast		
Unbalanced Diet		
Weigh Daily		
Drink Little Water		
Lack of Exercise		
Other		

Trigger Foods

Name your trigger foods. How do you feel after eating
these foods? What action do you need to take to change?

TRIGGER FOODS	HOW MY TRIGGER FOODS MAKE ME FEEL (1-10)	ACTION TO TAKE (1-10)
Chocolate		
Nuts		
Sugars		
Fatty Foods		
Salty Foods		
Pizza		
Mexican Foods		
Italian Foods		
Other Foods		

15

How to Stop the Bingeing

SELF EVALUATION:

1. **Evaluate my last binge without judging myself. What was I doing? Thinking? Feeling?**

2. **What did I learn from this binge that can be helpful in preventing binges?**

3. **Fears I have if I eliminate my bingeing:**

4. **Substitutions for bingeing I could use:**

EXERCISES:

1. Visualize yourself not bingeing. Make this happen. What feelings does this bring up for you? On a scale of 1-10, how do you feel after bingeing? After stopping a binge?

2. Visualize yourself being kind to you after you binge rather than beating yourself up. On a scale of 1-10, how do you feel when you beat yourself after a binge? How do you feel when you are kind and compassionate with yourself?

3. Prior to having your next binge, write in your journal your thoughts and feelings. This often interrupts the emergency of the binge.

Binge Diary

Write when and what you eat. What are your feelings before and after each binge? What action can you take to stop the bingeing?

DATE	WHAT I ATE	FEELINGS		ACTION TO TAKE (1-10)
		BEFORE A BINGE (1-10)	AFTER A BINGE (1-10)	

Thoughts to Prevent a Binge

Write your thoughts before and after each binge. Indicate on a scale from 1-10, how each thought makes you feel. What action can you take to stop the bingeing?

THOUGHTS BEFORE A BINGE (1-10)	THOUGHTS AFTER A BINGE (1-10)	ACTION TO TAKE TO CHANGE (1-10)
I'll just have a snack.		
I'll start a diet later.		
No one is around to notice my binge.		
No one cares about me so what's the use in trying?		
I am so stressed. I'll have a binge to make me feel better.		
I hate myself so I'll prove myself unworthy by bingeing		
Other		

Healthy Alternatives to Bingeing

Name causes of a binge. Then list alternatives to bingeing.

CAUSES OF A BINGE	ALTERNATIVES TO BINGEING
Boredom: Need for an activity instead of eating.	
Overwhelming Feelings (Anger, Sadness, Anxiety)	
Cause for Celebration	
Stress: Need for relaxation	
Other causes	

How to Stop the Purging

SELF EVALUATION:

1. When did I begin to purge?

2. When do I purge? What sets me up to purge?

3. When don't I need to purge?

4. What beliefs could I use to stop purging?

EXERCISES:

1. Visualize yourself not purging. Practice making this visualization be true for you. On a scale of 1-10, how do you feel when you purge? How would you feel if you stopped purging?

2. Recall the last time you purged. Rather than beating yourself up for purging, try to learn from it. What were you feeling prior to the purge? What are some alternatives you could use in place of purging?

3. Prior to purging, journal your thoughts and feelings. The writing can help take the place of bingeing or purging.

Purge Diary

Write what you eat and when you eat it. What are you feeling before
and after each purge? What action can you take to stop the purging?

DATE	WHAT I ATE	FEELINGS		ACTION TO TAKE (1-10)
		BEFORE A PURGE	AFTER A PURGE	

Thoughts to Prevent Purging

Indicate thoughts you had prior to your purge. What thoughts
could you use to prevent a purge? On a scale of 1-10, how does each
thought make you feel? What action do you need to take to change?

THOUGHTS PRIOR TO PURGING (1-10)	THOUGHTS TO USE INSTEAD OF PURGING (1-10)	ACTION TO TAKE TO CHANGE (1-10)
I'll eat all I can because I am going to purge anyway.		
If I purge, I'll not get fat.		
I'm going to purge so it doesn't matter what I eat.		
Purging helps me be less stressed.		
Purging is the only thing no one but me can control.		
If I purge, I can eat all I want.		
My life is so messed up I might as well purge.		
When I purge, I don't have to feel my pain.		
Other thoughts		

Food Diary

List the foods you eat daily according to the food pyramid group.

FOOD GROUP	BREAK-FAST	SNACK	LUNCH	SNACK	DINNER	SNACK
Bread, Cereal Rice and Pasta _(6-11 servings)_						
Vegetables _(3-5 Servings)_						
Fruits _(2-4 Servings)_						
Milk, Yogurt and Cheese _(2-3 Servings)_						
Meat, Poultry, Dry Beans Eggs and Nuts _(2-3 servings)_						
Fat and Sweets _(Use sparingly)_						

Tally of the Food Groups

Mark each time you eat the food category for the week.

	Mon	Tues	Wed	Thur	Fri	Sat	Sun	Total for the week
Bread Group *(6-11 Servings)*								
Vegetable Group *(3-5 Servings)*								
Fruit Group *(2-4 Servings)*								
Milk Group *(2-3 Servings)*								
Meat Group *(2-3 Servings)*								
Fat Group *(Use Sparingly)*								

To figure how many calories you can eat and still lose an average of one pound a week, multiply your current weight by 10.
Current weight in pounds_____ x 10=_____ calories

Physical Evaluation

Indicate your usual pattern of behavior related to your
physical self. What action do you need to take to make changes?

BEHAVIOR	USUAL PRACTICE (1-10)	ACTION TO TAKE (1-10)
Breakfast		
Lunch		
Dinner		
Food Guide Pyramid		
Lifestyle of Eating		
Eating Habits		
Speed of Eating		
Starvation		
Bingeing		
Purging		

BEHAVIOR	USUAL PRACTICE (1-10)	ACTION TO TAKE (1-10)
Body Image		
Body Awareness		
Love of Body		
Body Fat		
Use of Scales		
Exercise		
Medical Problems		
Medication		
Drugs /Alcohol		
Other		

C H A P T E R   T W O

Change Your Thoughts to
Change Your Weight and Self-esteem

Substitute the following irrational thoughts with a rational thought.

1. **Once I lose the weight I desire, my problems will be solved.**

2. **Eating is the only problem I have.**

3. **It is impossible for me to overcome this eating problem because my parents were not there for me.**

4. **What others think of me is more important than what I think.**

5. **How I look determines who I am.**

■■■

EXERCISES:

1. Draw a line down the middle of the paper. List your negative thoughts on the left side of the paper. On the right side of the paper list the positive statement. After you practice this, you will be able to do this in your mind without writing it. Do this same exercise, putting on one side of paper, thoughts which make you feel good vs. bad about yourself.

2. Write your thoughts and feelings in your journal. Then go back and underline your positive and negative thoughts with different colored pens. This will give you the opportunity to see your progress of having more positive than negative statements.

Change Negative to Positive Thoughts

NEGATIVE STATEMENT (Feel Bad About Self)	POSITIVE STATEMENT (Feel Good About Self)
I can't do anything right.	
I'm so fat and ugly.	
I'm stupid.	
I don't have any friends.	
I am stuck in this job because no one else would hire me.	
Everyone is prettier than me.	
Other Negative Thoughts	

Stinking Thinking

STINKING THINKING	USUAL PATTERN (1-10)	ACTION TO TAKE (1-10)
Perfect Thinking		
Irrational Thoughts		
Screen Thoughts		
Inflate /Deflate Thoughts		
Negative Thoughts		
Self-hate Thoughts		
Victim Thoughts		
Irresponsible Thoughts		
Other		

How to Stop Your Obsessive Thoughts

SELF EVALUATION:

1. If I were not obsessing about food, I would have to think about:

2. Beliefs I can have to lessen my obsessive thinking:

3. Fears of giving up my obsessive thoughts:

4. My obsessive thoughts influence my eating:

EXERCISES:

1. Wear a rubber band around your wrist and when you start to obsess about something, pull back the rubber band, snap your wrist gently and say, "Stop that thinking." Switch from obsessive thoughts to nurturing thoughts.

2. Visualize yourself with your obsessive thoughts. On a scale of 1-10, how does it feel? Now visualize yourself not having the obsessive thoughts. How much better does this feel? What action do you need to take to have this happen?

3. Write in your journal your feelings and thoughts. Underline with different colored pens when you are obsessive and when you are not. This allows you to see if you are making progress.

Obsessive Thoughts

Name your obsessive thoughts. What are thoughts you could
use to counter these thoughts? How do you feel when you use each?

OBSESSIVE THOUGHTS (1-10)	COUNTER OBSESSIVE THOUGHTS (1-10)	FEELINGS ABOUT THESE THOUGHTS (1-10)
Food		
Weight		
Exercise		
Work		
Relationships		
Past or Future		
Sex		
Money		
Other		

Overcome Your Perfectionism

SELF EVALUATION:

1. **Ways I was taught to be perfect:**

2. **Results of my trying to be perfect:**

3. **Beliefs which I could have to overcome my perfectionism:**

4. **Fears I have of giving up my perfectionism:**

5. **My perfection affects my eating:**

EXERCISES:

1. Visualize yourself without pressures you now have to be perfect. Imagine celebrating the fact that you made a mistake and learned from that mistake. On a scale of 1-10, how does this feel? How do you make this happen?

2. Write in your journal the ways you try to be perfect. After each, write what action you could take to be different. Use a colored pen to indicate when you are trying to be perfect and when you are not.

Perfection Chart

Name the ways you try to be perfect. Indicate how this
makes you feel. What action do you need to take to change?

WAYS I TRY TO BE PERFECT (1-10)	FEELINGS ABOUT BEING PERFECT (1-10)	ACTION TO TAKE TO CHANGE (1-10)
Physically		
Achievements		
Emotions		
Relationships		
Work		
Appearance		
Actions		
Thoughts		
Other		

33

Change "Shoulds" to "Choices"

SELF EVALUATION:

1. **When are the times I say I should do something?**

2. **How do I feel when I should do something? How do I feel when I have a choice?**

3. **What are the ambivalent feelings I have about making changes about my weight and eating?**

4. **What beliefs could I use to allow me more choices?**

5. **My living my life by "shoulds" instead of choices affects my eating:**

EXERCISES:

1. Visualize yourself having choices instead of leading your life full of "shoulds". On a scale of 1-10, how does it feel to live your life by "shoulds" vs. choices?

2. Write in your journal your feelings about living by "shoulds" and by choices. Underline with different colored pens the times you live by "shoulds" and the times you live by choices. This will allow you to become aware of how often and when you do not give yourself choices.

"Shoulds" vs. Choices Chart

Make a list of your "shoulds." After each "should," write choices
you can make. What action do you need to take to have more choices?

"SHOULDS" (1-10)	CHOICES (1-10)	ACTION TO TAKE (1-10)
Go on a Diet		
Go to Church		
Save Money		
Go Back to School		
Eat Slower		
Write Letters		
Learn a New Hobby		
Get New Friends		
Be Kinder to Others		
Other		

To Motivate Yourself, Take Action

SELF EVALUATION:

1. **What is my thinking that prevents me from motivating myself?**

2. **What fears do I have to motivate myself or take action?**

3. **When have I felt motivated in the past?**

4. **What is the different now from when I have been motivated in the past?**

5. **My lack of motivation affects my eating:**

EXERCISES:

1. Visualize yourself motivated. What is the first step you need to take to motivate yourself? How does it feel to lack motivation? Have motivation?

2. Write in your journal feelings and thoughts regarding your lack of motivation. Underline with different colored pens when you are motivated and when you are not.

Motivation Chart

List when you are motivated and when you are not.
What action do you need to take to change?

SITUATION	LACK OF MOTIVATION (1-10)	ACTION TO TAKE (1-10)
Work		
Change Jobs		
Lose Weight		
Healthier Eating		
Change Friends		
Exercise		
Get Life Organized		
Do Chores		
Write in Journal		
Other		

Use Visualization to Obtain Your Ideal Weight

SELF EVALUATION:

1. Dreams I have which I could visualize:

2. The area in my life that is the most difficult for me to visualize being any different:

EXERCISES:

1. Visualize yourself going to a family reunion as you now are. Imagine how you look and how you see yourself. What are you wearing? Who is at the reunion? Where is it? Take your time visualizing through your sense of sight. Next, imagine the sounds you hear. What are people saying to you? What is the music you hear? What is the background noise? Now imagine the sense of touch. What does the outfit you are wearing feel like? How does the sofa you are sitting on feel? Imagine all the things you can touch in the room. Now imagine the sense of smell. What food is there? What perfumes do you smell? What is your overall feeling about yourself and this experience? Now imagine yourself going to this reunion at your ideal weight. Imagine how you want to look. What are you seeing, smelling, touching, and feeling differently? You can react and feel differently when you visualize the changes. What feelings did this visualization bring up for you?

2. The next time you are upset and feel out of control, visualize yourself in a place and time when you were most comfortable with yourself and loved yourself the most. Visualize through sight, sound, smell, touch, and the overall feelings of that time. Bring those feelings to the surface as if you were at that place and time now. It is a very helpful thing to do. Some people like to visualize their marriage, the birth of their child (not the labor), or their ideal weight. When is a time you can bring beautiful memories to achieve these same feelings?

Daily Affirmations to Love Your Body and Self

Name an affirmation for the day, week, or month until you believe it.
What action do you need to take to make the affirmation come true for you?

DAILY AFFIRMATION	ACTION TO TAKE (1-10)
I love my body and self.	
I am worthwhile and lovable.	
I have the right to all my feelings.	
I have the right to make mistakes.	
I am special and unique.	
I can be angry with people I love.	
Relaxation is my right.	
Other's opinion of me is not my concern.	
I have the right to be happy.	
Other affirmations	

Thought Patterns

TYPE OF THINKING	USUAL PATTERN (1-10)	ACTION TO TAKE (1-10)
Perfect Thinking		
Obsessive Thinking		
Should vs. Choices		
Motivation		
Affirmations		
Visualization		
Creative Thinking		
Addictive Thinking		
Stinking Thinking		
Negative Thinking		
Other		

C H A P T E R   T H R E E

How to Express Your Feelings to
Change Your Weight and Self-esteem

SELF EVALUATION:

1. Ask myself before I eat, am I physically hungry or emotionally hungry? If I am physically hungry, eat. If I am emotionally hungry, ask what do I need emotionally?

2. Instead of eating to meet these emotional needs, I could:

3. Healthy eaters are different from me:

4. What needs does emotional eating provide for me? What are other ways to meet these needs?

▟▟▟

41

EXERCISES:

1. Visualize yourself eating for physical reasons instead of emotional reasons. How does this feel? The next time you start to eat for emotional reasons, ask yourself what you could do instead of eating.

2. Write in your journal other thoughts and feelings you have about your emotional hunger.

3. Paste a list of alternatives to eating on the refrigerator so that when you go to the refrigerator, there are other ideas of what you can do. Each time that you eat for emotional reasons, use this as way to learn more about yourself. If you don't try to understand what is going on, it will be difficult to change your behavior.

Eating for Physical vs. Emotional Needs

EATING FOR EMOTIONAL REASONS (1-10)	EATING FOR PHYSICAL REASONS (1-10)	ACTION TO TAKE TO CHANGE (1-10)
Bored/Tired		
Need Comforting		
Feeling Hopeless		
Stressed		
Happy/Sad		
Other		

Express Your Feelings

SELF EVALUATION:

1. **Underline the feelings you have trouble accepting. Circle those that you have trouble expressing.**

Anger	Energetic	Happiness	Nervous
Anxiety	Envious	Hurt	Optimistic
Contentment	Excitement	Jealous	Pain
Compassion	Fear	Joy	Persecuted
Depression	Guilt	Lonely	Sad
Despair	Hate	Love	Shame

2. **Fears I have in accepting and expressing my feelings.**

3. **Stuffing my feelings influences my eating:**

EXERCISES:

1. Imagine an unwelcome feeling and welcome it into your life. Write what you might say to this feeling, telling it why you have been scared of it. Now write your feelings as you accept this feeling. Imagine it as a healthy thing for you to accept this feeling. Repeat with other feelings until you get comfortable with feelings without having to judge them.

2. Visualize yourself expressing how you feel? What is a first step in doing this?

3. If it is difficult for you to identify your feelings, it may be helpful to start journal writing and underline feelings after you write about them. This helps you express your feelings. Underlining these feelings helps you to be aware of what you are feeling.

Grieve Your Losses

STEPS IN GRIEVING	USUAL PATTERNS (1-10)	ACTION TO TAKE (1-10)
Denial		
Anger		
Depression		
Willingness to Negotiate		
Acceptance of the Loss		

EXERCISES:

1. Allot a certain amount of time each day to journal, cry, get angry or whatever you need to do to grieve your losses.

2. Visualize yourself grieving your losses. Imagine yourself no longer feeling the pain, hurt, or loss that you now feel. On a scale of 1-10, how does that feel? What action do you need to take for this to happen?

3. Write a letter to that which you have lost. What do you need to say to this person, food, weight, or fat? Then pretend to be that person or thing you have lost. What do you need to hear from them?

Anger as Positive Energy

SELF EVALUATION:

1. **Ways I may block my anger:**

2. **Behaviors I have that create anger in my relationships:**

3. **Ways I can express my anger:**

4. **What would you like to say to your anger? What does your anger want to say to you?**

5. **My anger influences my eating:**

EXERCISES:

1. Visualize yourself letting go of your anger. Replace it with a pleasant thought. On a scale of 1-10, how does that feel?

2. Next time you are angry, write in your journal about it. Then talk to the person you are angry with so you don't have to keep it inside.

Anger Chart

List what makes you angry. How do you express anger?
What action do you want to take to lessen the anger?

CAUSES OF MY ANGER (1-10)	WAYS I EXPRESS MY ANGER (1-10)	ACTION TO TAKE (1-10)
Self		
Family		
Betrayal		
Jealousy		
Being Controlled		
Irrational Thoughts		
Friends		
Co-workers		
Unappreciated		
Other		

Sob the Sadness

SELF EVALUATION:

1. I express my sadness by:

2. My beliefs about sadness that would be helpful to me:

3. My fears in expressing my sadness:

4. My eating is related to my sadness by:

EXERCISES:

1. Take the last time that you felt sadness. What caused the sadness? What did you do about it? What could you have done differently? If needed, what do you still need to do to let go of the sadness?

2. Visualize yourself letting go of the sadness that you have from the past. On a scale of 1-10, how does this feel to let go of the sadness? What do you need to do to have this happen?

3. Write in your journal thoughts and feelings you have about sadness. Underline when you are sad so you can chart the causes and trends.

Sadness Chart

Chart what makes you sad. How do you react when you are sad?
What action do you need to take to help overcome the sadness?

CAUSES OF SADNESS (1-10)	REACTION TO SADNESS (1-10)	ACTION I CAN TAKE TO CHANGE (1-10)
Looks		
Weight		
Losses		
Loneliness		
Family		
Abuse		
Friends		
Past		
Other		

Decrease the Depression

SELF EVALUATION:

1. My signs of depression:

2. What family members have been depressed?

3. Beliefs that I could use to lessen my depression:

4. What are my fears of my depression?

5. My depression affects my eating:

EXERCISES:

1. Visualize yourself not being depressed, but doing things you enjoy. Reward yourself by doing pleasurable activities after you complete a couple things you don't want to do, but need to get done.

2. Make a list to organize things you can do to feel better. Prioritize the list. Keep it within reasonable limits. Put an "A" in front of what you have accomplished for the day and a "P" for pleasure received so that you become aware of your progress. It also helps you to make sure you balance your life with pleasures and achievements.

Depression Chart

CAUSES OF DEPRESSION (1-10)	ACTION TO TAKE (1-10)
Chemical Imbalance	
Negative Thoughts	
Hopelessness	
Lack of Exercise	
Unbalanced Diet	
Family Situation	
Losses	
Work	
Relationships	
Lack of Money	
Other	

Lessen the Anxiety and Fear

SELF EVALUATION:

1. I become anxious and afraid when:

2. My body shows me that I am anxious:

3. Beliefs that would help me become less anxious or fearful:

4. My fears and anxiety affect my eating:

EXERCISES:

1. The next time you feel anxious, take a deep breath. Breathe in through your nose and out through your mouth. This will help you to relax and be less anxious. You can also tense each set of your muscles, one at a time. After tightening your muscles, relax them.

2. Verbalize your feelings of fear to another. (It helps to lessen the fear.) Visualize yourself reacting to the fearful situation in the manner that you would like. Repeat with another fear.

3. Write in your journal about your fears and anxieties. Underline with different colored pens when you are fearful or anxious and when you are not.

Anxiety and Fear Chart

SITUATION	FEARS (1-10)	ANXIETY (1-10)	ACTION TO TAKE (1-10)
Weight			
Fat			
Eating			
Embarrassed			
Ridiculed			
The Fattest One			
Not the Best			
Perfection			
Relationships			
Health			
Other			

Stop the Guilt

SELF EVALUATION:

1. **What causes me to feel guilty?**

2. **Who makes me feel guilty? What can I do to not allow others to make me feel guilty?**

3. **Beliefs that influence my guilt:**

4. **Fears I have of letting go of my guilt:**

5. **My guilt affects my eating:**

EXERCISES:

1. Visualize yourself letting go of your guilt. Imagine the guilt leaving your body. Enjoy the light feeling that you experience by letting go of the heaviness of the guilt.

2. Write in your journal about your guilt. After writing in your journal, pretend you are someone else reading your journal. What would you say to this other person? Is that what you also need to say to yourself? You want to be as nice to yourself as you are to your friends. Underline when you are feeling guilty so that you can chart your progress.

Guilt Chart

What are the causes and purposes of your guilt? What
action can you take to change from feeling guilty to non-guilty?

CAUSES OF THE GUILT	PURPOSE OF THE GUILT (1-10)	ACTION TO TAKE TO CHANGE (1-10)
No Choices		
Irrational Thoughts		
Pleasing Others		
Imperfect		
Inadequate		
Unmotivated		
Relationships		
Sex		
Other		

Overcome the Shame

SELF EVALUATION:

1. I feel shame about:

2. I was shamed as a child:

3. Beliefs that I could have to eliminate my shame:

4. Fears that I have in letting go of my shame:

5. My shame affects my eating:

EXERCISES:

1. Visualize the feeling of not having the shame you now have. Let go of the shame as though you are tearing a page out of a notebook and crumbling it and throwing it away. Change your thoughts from "I deserve to be shamed" to "I don't need to have shame as a part of my life. I will feel better without it." On a scale of 1-10, how does this feel?

2. Write in your journal thoughts and feelings about your shame. Underline with different colors times when you are feeling shame and when you are not.

Shame Chart

What is the purpose of your shame? What behaviors result?
What action do you need to take to rid yourself of the shame?

PURPOSE OF SHAME (1-10)	BEHAVIORS (1-10)	ACTION TO TAKE (1-10)
Replaces Guilt		
Don't Feel Worthy		
Don't Have to do Anything		
Feeling Not Good Enough		
Wrong Doings		
Things I Say and Do		
Have Others Feel Sorry For Me		
Only Way I Know		
Other		

Lessen the Jealousy

SELF EVALUATION:

1. When do I feel jealous?

2. Beliefs that contribute to my jealousy:

3. Beliefs that could help me lessen my jealousy:

4. My fears in letting go of my jealousy:

5. My jealousy influences my eating:

EXERCISES:

1. Visualize yourself accepting your jealousy and letting go of it. On a scale of 1-10, how does it feel to let go of your jealousy?

2. Write in your journal your feelings and thoughts about your jealousy. Underline with different colored pens when you are jealous and when you are not. What trends do you see?

Jealousy Chart

CAUSES OF JEALOUSY *(Things and People)* (1-10)	ACTION TO TAKE TO CHANGE (1-10)
Feeling Inadequate	
Pretty People	
Thin People	
House, Cars and Things	
Popular People	
Articulate People	
Successful People	
Talented People	
People With Money	
Jewelry and Clothes	
Other	

Show Compassion to Yourself

SELF EVALUATION:

1. How do I treat myself differently than I do my best friend?

2. How would I like my parents or best friend to treat me?

3. What keeps me from treating myself this way?

4. What beliefs do I need to change in order for me to be able to show compassion for myself?

5. My eating is related to my lack of compassion for myself:

EXERCISES:

1. Evaluate the last time you were hard on yourself and didn't show any compassion. Now take the same situation and show compassion. What was the difference in how you felt after showing yourself compassion?

2. Visualize yourself showing compassion toward yourself. Imagine treating yourself in the most comforting, compassionate way you can.

3. Journal other thoughts and feelings you have regarding compassion.

Compassion Chart

BEHAVIORS	COMPASSION TO OTHERS (1-10)	COMPASSION TO SELF (1-10)	ACTION TO TAKE (1-10)
Forgiveness			
Perfection			
Weight			
Looks			
Hugs			
Kindness			
Mistakes			
Acceptance			
Losses			
Work			
Others			

Balance Contentment with Happiness

SELF EVALUATION:

1. **Circle the following which provides happiness for you. Underline those traits you would like to have, but don't have yet.**

Adventure	Health	Relationships
Assertive	Integrity	Self-esteem
Challenge	Money	Sexuality
Contribution to Society	Nature	Spirituality
Fun	Optimism	Work
Growth	Personal Goal	

2. **What areas of my life am I not content or happy?**

3. **What beliefs contribute to my lack of contentment or happiness?**

4. **What beliefs could allow me to be more content or happy?**

5. **My eating is related to my lack of contentment and happiness by:**

EXERCISES:

1. Visualize yourself content. On a scale of 1-10, how does this feel? What are you doing? Thinking? Feeling?

2. Journal other thoughts and feelings in regard to being happy and content.

Contentment and Happiness Chart

List what makes you feel content and happy so that you can distinguish the two.
What action do you need to take to be more content and happy?

BEHAVIORS	CONTENTMENT (1-10)	HAPPINESS (1-10)	ACTION TO TAKE (1-10)
Work			
Relaxation			
Weight			
Looks			
Leisure Time			
Hobbies			
Relationships			
Exercise			
Money			
Other			

Journal Writing

SELF EVALUATION:

1. Reasons I give to not write in my journal:

2. Benefits that might occur to me if I do write instead of bingeing:

EXERCISES:

1. Visualize yourself using your journal to write your inner thoughts. Imagine feeling much better, having a sense of relief after writing, and being your own best friend. On a scale of 1-10, how does this feel?

2. Keep a journal of your food, feelings, or thoughts. Some people find writing a food journal for a couple of weeks is helpful to gain control of their eating. If you do write what you eat, it can be helpful to use different colored highlighters for the various food groups.

My Journal

Emotional Evaluation

FEELINGS	CAUSES (1-10)	ACTION TO TAKE (1-10)
Anger		
Anxiety/Fear		
Guilt		
Grief		
Jealousy		
Sadness		
Hate/Love		
Depression		
Compassion		
Contentment		
Happiness		

C H A P T E R   F O U R

Improve Your Relationships to Change Your Weight and Self-esteem

Life Line-Family History

SELF EVALUATION:

1. My family differs from a healthy family:

2. What I learned from my family regarding who I am:

3. Eating habits and attitudes toward my body that I learned from my family, which I wish to continue and discontinue:

4. What messages did my family members give me about their bodies? My body?

■■■

5. **Fears I have that I will repeat my family's behaviors:**

6. **What other family members have similar problems with their weight as I do?**

7. **When did I first become concerned about my weight?**

8. **Name the significant points in my life when changes in my weight occurred.**

9. **My eating and weight is related to my family:**

EXERCISES:

1. Visualize yourself saying what you need to say to your family to let them know how you feel. Practice saying what you are going to say until you feel comfortable. Say what you need to say for your sake and don't expect a certain response. This is for you more than for them.

2. Write in your journal your feelings about your family. Write a letter to any family member you have something to say. You don't need to send the letter unless you think it would be helpful. Sometimes the writing is enough.

My Life Line

Indicate the weight of the family members at different ages. What are the trends?

AGE	SELF	MOM	DAD	GRAND-MOTHER	GRAND-FATHER
0-5					
6-12					
13-20					
21-30					
31-40					
41-50					
51-60					
61-70					
71- 80					
81- Death					

How to Develop Healthy Relationships

SELF EVALUATION:

1. **How is my lack of a relationship or a poor one causing me to get my emotional needs met through food?**

2. **What keeps me in this relationship or prevents me from getting into a healthy relationship?**

3. **Has food had the same importance to me when I have been in love ? What was different from what I experience now?**

4. **What beliefs would help me with my relationships?**

5. **My relationships with others influences my eating and my weight:**

EXERCISES:

1. Visualize yourself in a healthy intimate relationship. On a scale of 1-10, how does that feel? Good luck in finding such a relationship. What do you need to do to have this happen?

2. Journal your thoughts and feelings about present and past relationships. Write what you have learned from past relationships to help you not make the same mistakes again.

68

Past and Present Relationships

TYPE OF RELATIONSHIP	PAST RELATIONSHIP (1-10)	PRESENT RELATIONSHIP (1-10)	ACTION TO TAKE (1-10)
Parents			
Siblings			
Grandparents			
Friends			
Co-workers			
Partner			
Neighbors			
Pets			
Other			

How Abusive Relationships Affect Your Weight and Self-esteem

SELF EVALUATION:

1. My personal experience with abusing or being abused:

2. My beliefs regarding abuse:

3. Action I could take to no longer abuse or be abused:

4. Fears I have to get out of the abusive relationship:

5. My abusive relationships affect my eating:

EXERCISES:

1. Visualize yourself no longer being in an abusive situation. How does that feel? What changes do you need to make? What are you doing in the visualization you are not doing now?

2. Journal your thoughts and feelings about abusive relationships. Write a letter to the abuser or to the one being abused. You don't have to give the letter to the abuser or the one abused for it to be helpful to you.

Abuse Chart

TYPE OF ABUSE (1-10)	FEELINGS (Abuse or Abuser) (1-10)	ACTION TO TAKE (1-10)
Physical Abuse		
Emotional Abuse		
Verbal Abuse		
Social Abuse		
Psychological Abuse		
Spiritual Abuse		
Sexual Abuse		
Harassment		
On the Job Abuse		
Psychological Abuse		
Other		

How Your Co-dependence/Dependence/ Independence Affect Your Weight and Self-esteem

SELF EVALUATION:

1. The people in my life that I have co-dependent, dependent, and independent relationships with:

    a. *Co-dependent:*
    b. *Dependent:*
    c. *Independent:*

2. In what areas of my life do I take care of others? Myself?

    a. *Financial:*
    b. *Emotional:*
    c. *Sexual:*
    d. *Intellectual:*
    e. *Physically:*

3. Do I feel someone other than me is responsible for my feelings? Do I feel if someone else takes care of me, I will feel happy, lovable, and worthy? If so, I need to change by:

4. How is my behavior overtly controlling as the caretaker?

5. Beliefs that would be healthier for my independence or dependence needs:

6. My co-dependence, independence, or dependence influences my eating:

EXERCISES:

1. Visualize yourself having a healthy relationship, which encourages a balance of independence and dependence. On a scale of 1-10, how does that feel? What changes do you need to make for this to happen?

2. Journal your thoughts and feelings about your co-dependence, dependence, and independence. Underline with different colored pens when you are co-dependent, independent, and dependent.

Co-dependence, Dependence, and Independence Chart

PERSON	CO-DEP. (1-10)	DEP. (1-10)	INDEP. (1-10)	ACTION TO TAKE (1-10)
Self				
Partner				
Family				
Friends				
Co-workers				
Neighbors				
Others				

How Control Issues Affect Your Weight and Self-esteem

SELF EVALUATION:

1. **What are the ways I am controlling in my life and with others? How do I allow others to control me?**

2. **What are the areas of control in my life that I could let go?**

3. **Beliefs which would be helpful for my control or being controlled:**

4. **How can I structure my eating so I am not out of control? Too much in control?**

5. **My control issues affects my eating:**

EXERCISES:

1. Visualize yourself in control of your life and eating in the way that you desire. Visualize it and then practice it. What are you doing differently in the visualization from what you are doing now?

2. Write in your journal thoughts and feelings about your control issues. Underline with different colored pens when you are controlling and when you are being controlled.

Control Chart

CONTROL ISSUES	MY CONTROL (Self and Others) (1-10)	CONTROLLED BY OTHERS (1-10)	ACTION TO TAKE (1-10)
Food			
Self			
Partner			
Family			
Friends			
Work			
Pets			
House			
Sex			
Money			
Others			

How to Stop the People Pleasing
(Inner vs. Other Directed)

SELF EVALUATION:

1. **People in my life I try to please:**

2. **A problem pleasing others presents for me:**

3. **Beliefs I could use to help me become more inner-directed and less outer-directed:**

4. **Fears I have in becoming more inner-directed:**

5. **My lack of inner-directness and pleasing others affects my eating:**

EXERCISES:

1. Visualize yourself meeting your needs instead of trying to please others. Interview or observe people who you feel model a sense of inner-direction. Ask how they think and react to situations so you know how to change.

2. Write your thoughts and feelings in regard to your inner vs. outer-directness and pleasing others. Underline with different colored pens when you are pleasing yourself vs. others.

Inner/Outer-Directed Chart

CATEGORY	INNER-DIRECTED BEHAVIOR (1-10)	PEOPLE PLEASING BEHAVIOR (1-10)	ACTION TO TAKE (1-10)
Self			
Partner			
Siblings			
Children			
Parents			
Co-workers			
Authority			
Thoughts			
Neighbors			
Others			

Set Necessary Boundaries
(Who Owns the Problem?)

SELF EVALUATION:

1. **My issues of confusion with my boundaries:**

2. **My boundary issues began when:**

3. **People who do not respect my boundaries and ways they don't respect it:**

   a. Mother or father:
   b. Children:
   c. Spouse:
   d. Mother-in-law or father-in-law:
   e. Friends:

4. **Beliefs that would be helpful in setting necessary boundaries:**

5. **My fears in allowing others to resolve their own problems:**

6. **My boundary problems influence my eating:**

EXERCISES:

1. Visualize yourself not taking on others' problems as your own. What is a problem that you could let go? Let go of one situation. Then practice letting go of another.

2. Journal thoughts and feelings about setting appropriate boundaries and letting go of others' problems. After writing, underline with different colored pens when you are setting appropriate vs. inappropriate boundaries.

Boundary Chart

SITUATION	APPROPRIATE BOUNDARIES (1-10)	INAPPRO-PRIATE BOUNDARIES (1-10)	ACTION TO TAKE TO CHANGE (1-10)
Self			
Parents			
Children			
Partner			
Co-workers			
Friends			
Others			

Develop Support Systems

SELF EVALUATION:

1. Reaction I got as a child when I asked for support:

2. How did my family model asking for support?

3. My fears in getting support:

4. Feelings I have about getting support:

5. My lack of support affects my eating:

EXERCISES:

1. Visualize yourself surrounded by all the support you need. Feel the warmth and love of all these people. Enjoy them. Allow their support to enter into your being. How have you surrounded yourself differently in this visualization than you do in your daily life?

2. Journal thoughts and feelings about getting support. Underline with a pen the times it would be helpful to get support. What keeps you from asking for this support?

Support Chart

TYPES OF SUPPORT (1-10)	SUPPORT I NEED (1-10)	ACTION TO TAKE (1-10)
Family		
Friends		
Co-workers		
Intimacy		
Share		
Assistance		
Guidance		
Challenge		
Play-Have Fun		
Accepts My Feelings		
Physical contact		

Social Evaluation

NEEDS	USUAL BEHAVIOR (1-10)	ACTION TO TAKE TO CHANGE (1-10)
Let Go of the Past		
Relationships		
Intimacy		
Vulnerability		
Control		
Codependent/ Dependent/ Independent		
Lonely/Isolation		
Expectations Of Others		
People pleasing		
Boundary Issues		

C H A P T E R   F I V E

Improve Your Self-esteem to Change Your Weight

SELF EVALUATION:

1. Ways I look for my self-esteem from others:

2. Factors influencing my self-esteem:

3. Ways my self-esteem is determined besides my looks:

4. Ways I could improve my self-esteem:

5. My eating is related to my self-esteem:

■■■

EXERCISES:

1. Take a time in your life when you felt the best you ever felt about yourself. Let the confidence and enjoyment resurface in your life today. What was the situation where you felt the most confident and your self-esteem was the highest?

2. Write in your journal thoughts and feelings about your self-esteem. Underline with different colored pens when your self-esteem is high vs. low.

Self-esteem Chart

SITUATION	SELF-ESTEEM NOW (1-10)	SELF-ESTEEM GOAL (1-10)
Weight		
Career		
Partner		
Parents		
Children		
Friends		
Money		
Other		

How to Develop Self-Love Without Being Selfish or Selfless

SELF EVALUATION:

1. My family showed selfish, selfless, or self-love:

2. Fears I have about loving myself:

3. Beliefs that I have about loving myself:

4. My lack of self-love affects my eating:

EXERCISES:

1. Each time you go through a doorway say, "I am lovable." As the saying goes, "Fake it until you make it." Then continue to say, "I love myself. I think I am a pretty neat person."

2. Wear a rubber band and each time you say a negative statement about yourself, snap the band. Then change the negative statement to a loving, affirming statement.

3. Visualize yourself loving yourself. What are you doing in your visualization that you could incorporate in your life now?

4. Journal thoughts and feelings you have in regard to self-love, selfishness, and selflessness. Underline each with a different colored pen so you can chart your progress of becoming more loving and less selfish and selfless.

Self-love, Selfish, and Selfless Chart

AREAS OF CONCERN	SELF-LOVE (1-10)	SELFISH (1-10)	SELFLESS (1-10)	ACTION TO TAKE (1-10)
Food				
Weight				
Recreation				
Parents				
Partner				
Children				
Friends				
Job				
Money				
Spirituality				
Other				

Love the Parent, Adult, and Child Within

SELF EVALUATION:

1. **What does my child want to do, say, or need?**

2. **What does my critical parent do, say or need?**

3. **What does my nurturing parent do, say, or need?**

4. **What does my adult do, say, or need?**

5. **My eating is related to my critical parent within:**

6. **My eating is related to my nurturing parent within:**

7. **My eating is related to my adult within:**

8. My eating is related to my child within:

9. Action to take to care for my child within:

10. Action to take to allow my adult to help me be more rational:

11. Action to take to have my nurturing parent instead of my critical parent:

EXERCISES:

1. Close your eyes and relax. Imagine that child inside yourself. There is a child in you who wants to play, wants you to stop criticizing her, and wants to have her needs met. Listen to the child who says, "I am tired of being good and doing for others. I want my needs heard." Now imagine the parent inside of you. See the critical parent who says mean and nasty things to that child of yours. Take that critical parent and say, "NO MORE! I am not going to let you hurt my child anymore." Teach the critical parent to be nurturing and accepting. Substitute your critical parent with a nurturing parent who allows you to make mistakes, loves you unconditionally, and is always there to protect you from that critical parent. Now say, "Hello" to the adult in you who helps the child within to make decisions that are healthy for you. Thank your adult for helping make decisions the child within does not have the experience to make. Allow yourself to feel this child, nurturing parent, and adult within.

2. Visualize your inner child being nurtured by your nurturing parent.

3. Journal the thoughts and feelings you have in regard to loving your parent, adult, and child within. Underline each with a different colored pen.

Parent, Adult and Child Within Chart

AREAS OF CONCERN	CHILD WITHIN (1-10)	ADULT WITHIN (1-10)	CRITICAL PARENT WITHIN (1-10)	NURTURE PARENT WITHIN (1-10)	ACTION TO TAKE (1-10)
Strengths					
Weakness					
Awareness					
Expression					
Food					
Relation-ships					
Work					
Emotional					
Other					

Just Be
(Enjoy the Present)

SELF EVALUATION:

1. Reasons for not enjoying the present:

2. I used to enjoy the present when:

3. Beliefs I could use to help me enjoy the present:

4. My fears about enjoying the present:

5. My eating is related to the present:

EXERCISES:

1. Visualize yourself enjoying the present instead of worrying about the past or future. On a scale of 1-10, how does that feel?

2. Journal feelings and thoughts you have in regard to enjoying the present. Underline with a different colored pen when you are spending energy on the past, future and present.

Present, Past and Future Chart

TOPIC	PRESENT (1-10)	PAST (1-10)	FUTURE GOALS (1-10)	ACTION TO TAKE (1-10)
Food Habits				
Weight				
Recreation				
Parents				
Partner				
Children				
Friends				
Job				
Money				
Spirituality				
Other				

Identity to Include More Than What You Weigh

SELF EVALUATION:

1. **What is my identity besides my looks?**

2. **What are the beliefs and thoughts that cause me to feel as if my identity is tied to my looks?**

3. **What thoughts do I need to change to feel better about myself and have a healthier identity?**

4. **What are my fears in making this change?**

5. **My identity influences my eating:**

EXERCISES:

1. Visualize yourself making a change in your identity. You want to see yourself to be more than your weight. What is the first step you make? On a scale of 1-10, how does that feel? Good luck in making this change.

2. Write in your journal your thoughts and feelings you have about your identity. Underline the times your identity is besides your looks.

Identity Chart

SITUATION (1-10)	IDENTITY NOW (1-10)	IDENTITY GOALS (1-10)	ACTION TO TAKE (1-10)
Weight			
Appearance			
Job/Career			
Parent			
Partner			
Child			
Friend			
Intelligence			
Assertive			
Relaxation			
Other			

Psychological Evaluation

BEHAVIOR	USUAL PATTERN (1-10)	ACTION TO TAKE (1-10)
Self-esteem		
Self-love		
Selfish		
Selfless		
Critical Parent		
Nurturing Parent		
Child within		
Adult within		
Identity		
Enjoy the Present		

C H A P T E R   S I X

Enhance Your Spirituality to Change Your Weight and Self-esteem

Higher Power

SELF EVALUATION:

1. My higher power is:

2. My fear in having a higher power is:

3. My beliefs that prevent me from having a higher power:

4. My higher power could help me with my eating:

■■■

EXERCISES:

1. Take the last time you had a binge. Turn to your higher power for help. Have a dialogue with your higher power in regard to this binge. What would you say to your higher power? What would your higher power say to you? Write this in your journal or talk to an empty chair, pretending your higher power is in the chair. You can continue to have such a dialogue about any problems you have.

2. Take a brown paper bag and write "higher power" or "God bag" on it. The next time you feel discouraged or do not know what to do, write this problem down on a piece of paper. Place the paper and all the feelings in the bag with the problem. State to your higher power, "I am no longer able to deal with this problem. I give it to you to help me."

3. Visualize yourself having a higher power that guides and supports you. What would you like this higher power to be like? Allow it to be.

How Your Values Affect Your Weight and Self-esteem

Underline the values that are important to you. Circle those you would like.

Caring	Forgiving	Kind	Popular
Courageous	Generous	Lovable	Reliable
Dependable	Honest	Mature	Tolerant
Enthusiastic	Hopeful	Opinionated	Trusting
Faithful	Inquisitive	Patient	Worthy

Honesty and Its Effect on Your Weight and Self-esteem

SELF-EVALUATION:

1. My fears in being honest and dishonest:

2. My honesty and dishonesty affect my eating:

EXERCISES:

1. Visualize yourself being honest. On a scale of 1-10, how do you feel when you are dishonest? When you are honest?

2. Journal your feelings and thoughts in regard to your honesty. After each lie, write the truth several times until you get comfortable with the truth. Underline with different colored pens when you are honest and dishonest.

Honest and Dishonest Chart

SITUATION	HONEST BEHAVIOR (1-10)	DISHONEST BEHAVIOR (1-10)	ACTION TO TAKE (1-10)
Weight			
Food			
Parents			
Partner			
Children			
Friends			
Money			
Job/Career			

Forgive Yourself and Others

SELF EVALUATION:

1. Persons in my life I need to forgive:

2. Ways I need to forgive myself:

3. My greatest fear in forgiving others and myself:

4. How does my not forgiving myself influence my eating?

5. How does not forgiving others influence my eating?

EXERCISES:

1. Visualize yourself forgiving yourself and others. On a scale of 1-10, how does it feel not to be carrying this extra weight around?

2. Write in your journal a letter to the person or persons that you need to ask for their forgiveness. You may wish to send them your letter or you may want to ask for their forgiveness in person. It is also possible that writing about it is enough.

Forgiveness Chart

WHO/WHAT	WHEN	HOW IT FEELS (1-10)	ACTION TO TAKE (1-10)
Self			
Partner			
Children			
Parents			
Friends			
Co-workers			
Weight			
Body			
Health			
Past			
Other			

Develop Patience with Yourself and Others

SELF EVALUATION:

1. What are the areas of my life when I am the most impatient with myself?

2. What role models do I have that respond differently than I do?

3. What are my fears in being patient? Impatient?

4. How is my eating related to my lack of patience?

EXERCISES:

1. Visualize yourself with a lot of patience toward yourself with regard to food and your body. What are you doing in this visualization that you can do in real life? On a scale of 1-10, how does that feel? What do you need to do to make this happen?

2. Visualize yourself being patient with others. What are you doing in this visualization that you can do?

3. Write in your journal thoughts and feelings you have related to developing more patience. Underline with different colored pens when you are patient vs. impatient.

Patience and Impatience Chart

PERSON OR THING	PATIENCE	IMPATIENCE (1-10)	ACTION TO TAKE (1-10)
Self			
Partner			
Children			
Parents			
Friends			
Co-workers			
Boss			
Changes			
Money			
Chores			
Other			

Trust and Its Effect on Your Weight and Self-esteem

SELF EVALUATION:

1. When do I trust myself? Others?

2. When do I not trust myself? Others?

3. Beliefs I have in regard to trust:

4. Fears I have to trust:

5. How does my lack of trust influence my eating?

EXERCISES:

1. Visualize trusting yourself and others. Take a situation where you distrust the most and imagine yourself reacting in a very different way than you usually do. What action do you need to take to have this happen?

2. Write in your journal about trust and mistrust. Underline with different colored pens when you trust vs. mistrust.

Trust vs. Mistrust Chart

PERSON OR THINGS	TRUST (1-10)	MISTRUST (1-10)	GOALS AND ACTION TO TAKE (1-10)
Self			
Partner			
Children			
Parents			
Friends			
Co-workers			
Boss			
Neighbors			
Weight			
Others			

How to Have Hope

SELF EVALUATION:

1. What has helped me in the past to be hopeful?

2. What beliefs could I have to make me feel hopeful?

3. What are my fears in being hopeful? Hopeless?

4. How does my hopelessness influence my eating?

5. How does my hope affect my eating?

EXERCISES:

1. Visualize yourself feeling hopeful instead of hopeless. On a scale of 1-10, how does this feel? See yourself achieving what you want.

2. Write about hope in your journal. Underline with different colored pens when you are hopeful vs. feeling hopeless. See if you can see any trends.

Hope vs. Hopeless Chart

SITUATION	HOPEFUL (1-10)	HOPELESS (1-10)	ACTION TO TAKE (1-10)
Weight			
Eating			
Career			
Depression			
Partner			
Family			
Parents			
Co-workers			
Money			
Life in General			
Other			

Spiritual Evaluation

BEHAVIOR	USUAL PATTERN (1-10)	ACTION TO TAKE TO CHANGE (1-10)
Higher Power		
Caring		
Faithful		
Forgiveness		
Honesty		
Hope		
Trust		
Patience		
Courage		
Love		
Other		

C H A P T E R   S E V E N

Love Your Sexuality to Change Your Weight and Self-esteem

SELF EVALUATION:

1. **I wish to change my thoughts regarding my sexuality:**

2. **Fears I have in regard to my sexuality:**

3. **My sexual energy influences my weight, body image, and eating:**

EXERCISES:

1. Visualize yourself being comfortable with your sexuality. What is different in your visualization from what is happening in your life?

2. Write in your journal your feelings and thoughts about your sexuality. Underline with a different colored pen when you indicate comfortable vs. uncomfortable feelings of sexuality.

▬▬▬

Sexuality Chart

BEHAVIORS	COMFORT WITH SEXUALITY (1-10)	UNCOMFORT-ABLE WITH SEXUALITY (1-10)	ACTION TO TAKE (1-10)
Talking About Sex			
Hugging			
Nakedness			
Initiating/ Responding to Love Making			
Touching			
Foreplay			
Climax			
Clothes			
Other			

Overcome the Trauma of Sexual Abuse

SELF EVALUATION:

1. I was sexually abused by:

2. Why I am afraid to talk about my abuse:

3. My beliefs related to my sexual abuse:

4. Beliefs I could use to help me overcome my sexual abuse:

5. My sexual abuse affects my eating, weight and body image:

EXERCISES:

1. Write a letter to your abuser telling him how you feel. You don't need to send the letter for it to be helpful to you. If you wish to confront your abuser, practice saying what you want to say. It may be helpful to practice with a friend first. How does this feel?

2. Visualize yourself letting go of the sexual abuse that was done to you as a child. You no longer give the abuser any power and you are free of the past. Give this to your higher power to be free.

Sexual Abuse Chart

SEXUAL ABUSE SYMPTOMS	SEXUAL ABUSE BEHAVIORS (1-10)	SEXUAL ABUSE GOALS (1-10)	ACTION TO TAKE (1-10)
Dissociation			
Anger or Fear of the Opposite Sex			
Seductive			
Fear of Genital Exam			
Promiscuous			
Aversion to Sex			
Sexual Identity Confusion			
Dreams of Sexual Assault			
Other			

Victimization No More

SELF EVALUATION:

1. I was victimized as a child:

2. When are the times I feel like a victim as an adult?

3. Beliefs I can use to no longer feel like a victim:

4. I am afraid to give up my victim role:

5. When I feel like a victim, it influences my eating:

EXERCISES:

1. Visualize yourself out of the victim role. You are no longer powerless, but powerful. You respond to your needs instead of pleasing others. How does this feel to you?

2. In your journal, write other thoughts and feelings you have about being a victim. Underline with different colored pens when you feel like a victim and when you do not.

Victimization Chart

BEHAVIORS	HOW I ALLOW MYSELF TO BE VICTIMIZED (1-10)	GOALS (1-10)	ACTION TO TAKE TO CHANGE (1-10)
Self			
Partner			
Parents			
Friends			
Children			
Job/Career			
Sexual			
Assertiveness			
Choices			
Others			

Value Your Male and Female Traits

SELF EVALUATION:

1. Male traits I value in myself include:

2. Female traits I value in myself include:

3. Beliefs I could use to develop both my maleness and femaleness:

4. Fears I have about developing my masculine and feminine traits:

5. My masculine and feminine traits influence my eating:

EXERCISES:

1. Visualize yourself developing your feminine and masculine traits. How do you see yourself differently in your visualization than you are now? What feelings does this bring up for you?

2. Write in your journal about your feminine and masculine traits. What do you need to do to have a balance with these traits? Underline with different colored pens when you exhibit masculine vs. feminine traits.

Male and Female Traits

TRAITS	COMFORT WITH MALE TRAITS (1-10)	COMORT WITH FEMALE TRAITS (1-10)	ACTION TO TAKE (1-10)
Assertiveness			
Competitive			
Caring/Loving			
Sensitive			

Sexual Evaluation

BEHAVIOR	USUAL PATTERN (1-10)	ACTION TO TAKE (1-10)
Sexuality		
Sexual Abuse		
Victimization		
Male/Female Traits		

C H A P T E R E I G H T

Assertive Skills to Change Your Weight and Self-esteem

SELF EVALUATION:

1. **It's difficult for me to give and receive compliments when:**

2. **It is difficult for me to express personal opinions because:**

3. **It is difficult for me to refuse requests because:**

4. **Fears I have of becoming assertive:**

5. **My lack of assertiveness affects my eating:**

◼◼◼

EXERCISES:

1. Take a situation in which you were passive. Visualize yourself being assertive in that situation. What would you say? Practice saying it until you can feel comfortable with it.

2. Take a situation in which you were aggressive. Visualize yourself being assertive in that situation. What would you say? On a scale of 1-10, how does it feel to be aggressive? Assertive?

3. Visualize yourself being assertive at times when it is difficult for you. Practice what you would do and say, then do it. Start with being assertive with people you do not know and do not care what they think.

4. Go through your journal and mark with different colored markers the times you were assertive, passive, and aggressive.

Assertive vs. Aggressive Charts

COMMENTS	AGGRESSIVE RESPONSES (1-10)	ASSERTIVE RESPONSES (1-10)
Should you be eating that dessert?		
You'd rather be fat than thin?		
I'd date you if you would lose weight.		
You've gained weight.		

Passive, Aggressive and Assertive Responses

SITUATION	PASSIVE RESPONSES (1-10)	AGGRESSIVE RESPONSES (1-10)	ASSERTIVE RESPONSES (1-10)
Self			
Partner			
Parents			
Children			
Friends			
Authority			
Co-workers			
Recreation			
Sexually			
Driving			
Other			

Avoid Manipulating or Being Manipulated

SELF EVALUATION:

1. **Beliefs I have that contribute to my manipulation of others:**

2. **Beliefs I have that contribute to my being manipulated:**

3. **Beliefs I could use to help me with my manipulating or being manipulated.**

4. **Fears I have about changing my behavior regarding manipulation:**

5. **How my being manipulated affects my eating:**

6. **How my manipulating others affects my eating:**

EXERCISES:

1. Visualize yourself not being manipulated or not manipulating. What would you do differently? Practice it over and over again until it becomes second nature to you.

2. Write in your journal about being manipulated or manipulating others. Underline with different colored pen examples when you manipulate others and when you are manipulated.

Manipulation Chart

SITUATION	MANIPULATE OTHERS (1-10)	MANIPULTED BY OTHERS (1-10)	ACTION TO TAKE (1-10)
Self			
Partner			
Parents			
Children			
Friends			
Authority			
Co-workers			
Recreation			
Sexually			
Stress			
Other			

119

Say No

SELF EVALUATION:

1. When are the times it is difficult to say no?

2. When is it easy to say no?

3. Beliefs I could have to say no:

4. Fears I have to say no:

5. My inability to say no affects my eating:

EXERCISES:

1. Say no to a person you believe would accept your no. Then practice with another person until you are comfortable with saying no.

2. Visualize yourself saying no when it has been difficult in the past. What could you have said? Practice this over and over in your mind until you can do it.

3. Write in your journal other thoughts and feelings you have to say no. Underline with different colored pens the times you are and are not able to say no.

"No" Responses

SITUATION	"NO" RESPONSES (1-10)	EFFECT ON ME (1-10)	ACTION TO TAKE (1-10)
Self			
Partner			
Parents			
Children			
Friends			
Authority			
Co-workers			
Recreation			
Want Something			
Feel Inadequate			
Other			

Send "I" Messages

SELF-EVALUATION:

1. When do I use "I" messages?

2. When do I use "you" messages?

3. How do "you messages" make me feel?

4. How do "I" messages affect my eating?

5. How do "you" messages affect my eating?

EXERCISES:

1. Think about the last time you sent a "you" message. What was the result? How can you send this as an "I" message? Visualize yourself sending "I" messages instead of "you" messages. On a scale of 1-10, how does this feel?

2. Write in your journal thoughts and feelings about when others send "you" messages and how you feel when others send "I" messages. This will help you better understand how others feel when you send a "you" versus "I" message.

"I" Messages

Indicate how you feel about the situation and the effect it has on you.

"YOU" MESSAGES	"I" MESSAGES
You are too fat.	
You are an idiot.	
You make mistakes.	
Your starving is crazy.	
Your purging is disgusting.	
Stop complaining.	
You have no self-control.	
You are so selfish.	
You are a slob.	
You look awful.	
You are too skinny.	

How to Maintain Your Power

SELF EVALUATION:

1. Times I feel most empowered:

2. Times I give my power away:

3. Beliefs I could have to become more empowered:

4. Fears I have in becoming empowered? Giving my power away?

5. My lack of power affects my eating:

EXERCISES:

1. Take an assertiveness class to help you become more comfortable with being assertive.

2. Take a situation in which you felt you had no power. Visualize yourself feeling powerful in this same situation. Visualize what you say, feel, and hear. Practice doing it. Repeat this with a different situation.

3. Write in your journal other feelings and thoughts you have about being powerful. Underline times when you feel powerful and when you do not. What are the trends?

Powerless and Power Chart

SITUATION	FEEL POWERFUL (1-10)	FEEL POWERLESS (1-10)	ACTION TO TAKE (1-10)
Self			
Partner			
Parents			
Children			
Friends			
Authority			
Co-workers			
Recreation			
Weight			
Eating			
Other			

Assertiveness Evaluation

SITUATION	USUAL PATTERN (1-10)	ACTION TO TAKE (1-10)
Give Compliments		
Receive Compliments		
Express Opinions		
Manipulation		
Say No		
Send "I" Messages		
Send "You" Messages		
Empowerment		
Feelings Expressed		
Feelings Stuffed		
Other		

C H A P T E R   N I N E

Reduce Stress to Change Your Weight and Self-esteem

Signs of Stress

SELF EVALUATION:

1. What are the signs when I am stressed?

2. My fears affect my stress:

3. My stress affects my eating:

EXERCISES:

1. Before an event at which you expect to be stressed, visualize what may take place. Then visualize how you can react in a less stressed way. When the event occurs, you will have prepared yourself to react the way you wanted.

2. Be kind to yourself during a tense situation. Do not dwell on the poor aspects of your performance. Dwell on what you did well and what you accomplished. After the tense situation, relax and celebrate it being over.

■■■

Stress Chart

CAUSES (1-10)	EFFECT ON ME (1-10)	ACTION TO TAKE TO CHANGE (1-10)
Self		
Partner		
Parents		
Children		
Authority		
Friends		
Work		
Leisure Time		
Money		
Sex		
Other		

Relaxation

SELF EVALUATION:

1. What do I do to relax?

2. What are forms of relaxation I would like to do? What keeps me from doing it?

3. What is the relationship of my eating and lack of relaxation?

EXERCISES:

1. Use any of the following techniques prior to eating. When you are tense, identify what is bothering you at that moment. Smile and say to yourself, *"I am not going to let this bother my body. I am going to protect my body."*

2. Scan your body to sense your tense or uncomfortable spots (for example, stomach, head, and shoulders). Loosen this area up a little by tensing and then relaxing the area.

3. Switch your thoughts to your breathing. Take two deep breaths from your abdomen through your nose and exhale slowly through your mouth. As you exhale the second breath, let your jaw go limp. You can use this technique at work to help you relax.

4. Hold each muscle group in a tensed position for ten seconds and then relax it for 45-60 seconds. Repeat with one muscle group before going to the next muscle group.

Relaxation Techniques

BODY PART	STRESS (1-10)	ACTION TO TAKE (1-10)
Hands and Forearms		
Biceps		
Triceps		
Face		
Neck and Throat		
Shoulders		
Chest		
Stomach		
Buttocks		
Legs		
Thighs		

Play (Have Fun)

SELF EVALUATION:

1. **When was the last time you played or had fun? What did you previously do that you could do again?**

2. **What does the child within want to do that you don't allow her to do? What keeps you from playing and having fun?**

3. **What beliefs could you have that would allow you to have fun and play?**

4. **My fears in playing and having fun:**

5. **My eating is related to my not having fun:**

EXERCISES:

1. Visualize yourself playing and having fun. What are ways you could have fun? On a scale of 1-10, how does this feel? What keeps you from taking this action?

2. Journal other thoughts and feelings in regard to your playing and having fun. Underline with different colored pens when you are playing and having fun and when you are not.

Fun Chart

USUAL BEHAVIOR (1-10)	GOALS TO HAVE FUN (1-10)	ACTION TO TAKE TO CHANGE (1-10)
Recreation		
Hobbies		
Sports		
Music		
Arts		
Plays		
Exercise		
Creativeness		
Friends/Family		
Other		

Stress Journal

Choose a stressful situation and use the following journal to learn from the stress.

SITUATION *(Who, What, When, Where?)*

PHYSICAL REACTIONS *(Tightness, Frown, Rapid Breathing)*

EMOTIONS *(Fear, Anger, Anxiety, Guilt)*

THOUGHTS *(Self-talk to Self and Others)*

BEHAVIORS *(Grit Teeth, Clinch Fists, Shout, Cry)*

BEHAVIORS I COULD CHANGE *(Action to Take)*

POSSIBLE SOLUTIONS *(Answer to Problem)*

Find a Balance in Your Life

BEHAVIOR	USUAL PRACTICE (1-10)	ACTION TO TAKE (1-10)
Food Pyramid Group		
Thinking vs. Feelings		
Expressed vs. Controlled Emotions		
Family vs. Friends		
Family vs. Work		
Alone vs. With Others		

BEHAVIOR	USUAL PRACTICE (1-10)	ACTION TO TAKE (1-10)
Quiet vs. Active		
Child vs. Adult vs. Parent Within		
Spiritual vs. Non-Spiritual		
Passive vs. Aggressive vs. Assertive		
Feminine vs. Masculine Traits		
Stressed vs. Relaxation		
Work vs. Play		

Stress/Relaxed Evaluation

BEHAVIOR	USUAL PATTERN (1-10)	ACTION TO TAKE (1-10)
Awareness of Stress		
Types of Stress		
Muscle Relaxation		
Relaxation Techniques		
Play and Fun		
Other		

C H A P T E R   T E N

Enrich Your Career to Change Your Weight and Self-esteem

Career Analysis

SELF EVALUATION:

1. What do I like about my job? Dislike about it?

2. What can I change about the job I now have? Career change?

3. What are my fears in making a change in my job? Career?

4. How does my career affect my eating?

▰▰▰

EXERCISES:

1. Visualize yourself in your ideal career and job situation. Imagine the work you would do, the work environment, the opportunity to be yourself and everything you want from the job. Go for it.

2. Journal other thoughts or feelings in regard to your career. Underline with different colored pens when you feel happy with your job and when you don't.

Career Analysis Chart

CAREER TRAITS	PRESENT JOB OR CAREER (1-10)	PAST CAREERS (1-10)	ACTION TO TAKE (1-10)
Likes			
Dislikes			
Strengths			
Weakness			
Skills			
Successes			
Failures			
Other			

138

Maximize Your Strengths and Minimize Your Weaknesses

SELF EVALUATION:

1. **Have a supervisor or someone who knows you well circle those characteristics she feels best describe you. Then underline those descriptions that you think describe you. Cross out your weaknesses since you are not going to dwell on them.**

Accepting	Congenial	Genuine	Organized
Achieving	Conscientious	Good-natured	Outgoing
Active	Considerate	Helpful	Patient
Adventurous	Cooperative	Humorous	Perceptive
Affectionate	Creative	Happy	Persistent
Ambitious	Dependable	Independent	Self-confident
Articulate	Determined	Insightful	Sociable
Assertive	Energetic	Intelligent	Spontaneous
Caring	Enthusiastic	Intuitive	Thoughtful
Cheerful	Friendly	Likeable	Trusting
Compassion	Gentle	Open-minded	Warm

2. **List other qualities that describe your strengths and weaknesses.**

   a. Strengths:

   b. Weaknesses:

3. **Beliefs I have which keep me from feeling good about my strengths.**

4. **Beliefs I could use to further my strengths:**

5. **Emphasizing my weaknesses instead of strengths affects my eating:**

139

EXERCISES:

1. Visualize yourself feeling your strengths and not worried about your
   weaknesses. What does that feel like? Each time you get into your car, remind
   yourself of these strengths to help you feel good about yourself.

2. Journal your thoughts and feelings in regard to your strengths and weaknesses.
   Underline with a different colored pen your strengths vs. weaknesses.

My Strength and Weakness on the Job

TRAITS	STRENGTHS (1-10)	WEAK- NESSES (1-10)	TIME SPENT (1-10)	ACTION TO TAKE (1-10)
Personality				
Intelligence				
Quickness				
Details				
Creative				
Follow Directions				
Others				

Skills

SELF EVALUATION:

1. **First, have a co-worker, boss, or friend, circle those skills she believes best describe you. Then underline those skills that you think best describe you. Give these skills the same importance that you do your weight and appearance. The result is you will feel better about yourself.**

Act as liaison	Count	Fun	Observe
Analyze	Design	Initiate	Organize
Classify	Entertain	Interview	Perceptive
Clarify	Evaluate	Make decisions	Proofread
Counsel	Expedite	Negotiate	Supervise

2. **What are the differences between how I perceive myself and how my co-worker or a friend perceives me? What do I think of a person who has these circled traits?** *(Remember this is you.)*

3. **How can I change my beliefs so I believe in myself?**

4. **How does not using my skills influence my eating?**

EXERCISES:

1. Visualize yourself in a career that emphasizes your skills. What keeps you from being in such a career?

2. Journal other thoughts and feelings about your skills. Underline when you identify a skill that you have.

Skills Chart

SKILLS (1-10)	CAREER CHOICES USING MY SKILLS (1-10)	ACTION TO TAKE TO CHANGE (1-10)
People		
Organizer		
Leader		
Hands		
Brain		
Follower		
Creative		
Personality		
Details		
Sees Big Picture		
Other		

Learn from Past Successes and Failures

SELF EVALUATION:

1. What have been my career successes in the past?

2. What failures on the job have I experienced in the past?

3. What are my fears of success?

4. What are my fears of failing?

5. How is my eating related to my successes and failures?

EXERCISES:

1. Visualize yourself as successful. What must you do to achieve it? YOU CAN DO IT! Good luck.

2. Write your feelings and thoughts about your successes and failures. See if you can see a pattern. What does this tell you that you need to do in order to succeed?

143

Successes and Failures on the Job

TRAITS	PAST SUCCESSES (1-10)	PAST FAILURES (1-10)	WHAT I LEARNED AND ACTION TO TAKE TO CHANGE (1-10)
Co-workers			
Boss/ Authority			
Reliable			
Promotions			
Salary			
Responsible			
Promptness			
Popular			
Relationships			
Other			

Parenting: Your Career?

SELF EVALUATION:

1. What are my needs about parenting and a career?

2. What changes would be helpful for me to make?

3. Action I can take to become a better parent:

4. Beliefs that would help me become a better parent:

5. Eating is related to my parenting:

EXERCISES:

1. Visualize yourself as a full-time parent or having a part-or full-time job. On a scale of 1-10, how does it feel to be able to spend the amount of time you wish with your children?

2. Journal other thoughts and feeling in regard to you being a parent.

3. List your strengths and weaknesses as a parent. Underline with different colored pens areas you are strong vs. weak.

Parenting Chart

BEHAVIOR	PARENTAL DESIRES (1-10)	CAREER DESIRES (1-10)	ACTION TO TAKE TO CHANGE (1-10)
Stay at Home			
Work at Home			
Work ½ Time			
Work Full-time			
Be Own Boss			
Prestige			
Travel			
Flex Hours			
Money			
Other			

Workaholic

SELF EVALUATION:

1. **Advantages and disadvantages to be a workaholic:**

2. **Beliefs I have regarding my workaholic behavior:**

3. **Beliefs I could use to help me with my workaholic behavior:**

4. **Fears I have to change my work addiction:**

5. **My eating is related to my work addiction:**

EXERCISES:

1. Visualize you (or your partner) no longer being a workaholic. On a scale of 1-10, how does that feel? What do you need to do to see that this visualization comes true?

2. Write in your journal thoughts and feelings about your (or your partner's) workaholic behavior. Practice saying what you need to say to your spouse after writing the letter.

Workaholic Chart

WORKAHOLIC TRAITS (1-10)	EFFECT ON ME (1-10)	ACTION TO TAKE (1-10)
All Energy Used at Work		
Lack of Relaxation		
Impatient with Others		
Last to Leave Work		
Always in a Hurry		
Perfectionist		
Guilty When Not Working		
Pleasures Only At Work		
Identity is Tied To Work		
Goal Vs. Process Oriented		
Other		

Set Realistic Goals

SELF EVALUATION:

1. **List of my dreams:**

2. **List of my needs:**

3. **Resources I have (assets in personality traits, friends, financial resources, education, time and energy) to reach my goals:**

4. **Fears I have in setting goals:**

5. **My eating and weight are related to my lack of career goal setting:**

EXERCISES:

1. Visualize yourself accomplishing your goals. Take one goal at a time and decide how you can reach it. Repeat with your next goal.

2. Write in your journal goals for yourself. Which one do you need to start in order to succeed?

Goals

EATING GOALS	
Today	
Week	
Month	
Year	
5 Years	
PERSONAL GOALS	
Today	
Week	
Month	
Year	
5 years	

CAREER GOALS	
Today	
Week	
Month	
Year	
5 Years	
OTHER GOALS	
Today	
Week	
Month	
Year	
5 Years	

Career Evaluation

SITUATION	USUAL PATTERN (1-10)	ACTION TO TAKE (1-10)
Career Analysis		
Career Strengths		
Career Weaknesses		
Career Successes		
Career Failures		
Skills		
Workaholic		
Parenting as a Career		

Tools

TOOLS	ACTION TO TAKE (1-10)
1. Follow food guide pyramid.	
2. Lifetime changes in eating.	
3. Eat slowly.	
4. Limit fat in your diet.	
5. Eat when physically hungry.	
6. Think abundance.	
7. Eat 3 meals and 2 snacks.	
8. Drink 8 glasses water daily.	
9. Say you love your body and self.	
10. Accept body today.	
11. Stop the alcohol and drug abuse.	
12. Have a yearly physical.	
13. Use anti-depressant if appropriate.	
14. Exercise moderately.	
15. Stop the stinking thinking.	
16. Snap wrist when think negatively.	
17. Give yourself permission to error.	
18. Visualize yourself at ideal weight.	
19. Use daily affirmations.	
20. Identify and express feelings.	
21. Write in journal.	
22. Grieve losses.	
23. Do not judge feelings.	
24. Express feelings, not stuff them.	

TOOLS	ACTION TO TAKE (1-10)
25. Eliminate unhealthy relationships.	
26. Develop healthy relationships.	
27. Understand family's role in eating.	
28. Balance time alone with others.	
29. Stop the people pleasing	
30. Let go of control issues.	
31. Set appropriate boundaries.	
32. Develop support systems.	
33. Accept and love yourself.	
34. Have identity be more than weight.	
35. Love parent, adult and child-within.	
36. Enjoy the present.	
37. Use a higher power.	
38. Forgive yourself and others.	
39. Be patient, trustful, and hopeful.	
40. Be courageous, honest and reliable.	
41. Accept and enjoy sexuality.	
42. Stop playing the victim role.	
43. Accept your female and male traits.	
44. Be assertive.	
45. Avoid being passive or aggressive.	
46. Say no when need to do so.	
47. Send "I" messages.	
48. Avoid "you" blame messages.	
49. Avoid manipulating others.	
50. Avoid being manipulated.	
51. Have fun and play.	
52. Use relaxation techniques.	
53. Balance your life.	
54. Career emphasizing strengths.	
55. Career emphasizing skills.	
56. Set realistic goals.	

Inter-relationship of Physical Self With Other Aspects of Self

In each box, indicate how your physical self is influenced by each of the other aspects of yourself. For example, what thoughts influence your physical being.

PARTS OF SELF	PHYSICAL (*Weight and Eating*)
Intellectual *Thoughts*	
Emotional *Feelings*	
Social *Relationships*	
Psychological *Identity*	
Spiritual *Faith*	
Sexual *Sexuality*	
Assertive *Express needs*	
Stress *Relaxation*	
Career *Roles*	

155

INDEX

About the Author

Sharon Sward is a Licensed Professional Counselor. She has a masters in counseling, masters in child development and family relations, and two years of a doctorate in counseling. Sharon is president of the Eating Disorder Professionals of Colorado and a member of the Academy of Eating Disorders, National Eating Disorder Organization, and the National Association of Anorexia Nervosa and Associated Disorders. Prior to becoming a counselor, Sharon was a university professor at the University of Tennessee, University of Georgia, California State University at Los Angeles, and Red Rocks Community College. Swimming, water aerobics, spinning, bicycling, skiing and hiking are sports Sharon enjoys. Other interests are reading, music, going to plays and sport events. She hopes to try ski diving in the future.

As a professional counselor and university professor, she had always been successful in her career and wondered why she couldn't have this same success with her weight. She once believed that her worth and her identity revolved solely around her weight. No matter what she weighed, she was never satisfied. Only when she was able to make the shifts that are mentioned in this book was she able to see and value her true worth.

As Sharon worked with her clients through the years, she noted their common characteristics, concerns and solutions. The solutions that worked for them are compiled in this book. Sharon wishes you well in your journey to make your dreams come true and for you to become more than what you weigh. If she can be more than what she weighs, you can too.

Sharon has presented workshops and keynote addresses throughout the country. She has been on numerous radio and television shows nationally, with plans to do many more shows. She hopes to meet many of you on her book tours and at conferences where she speaks. Feedback you might have regarding her books would be greatly appreciated. Sharon may be contacted at the following address. If you would like a CD or disk, use her email or home page address.

TO CONTACT THE AUTHOR OR ORDER CD OR DISK

Sharon Sward
% Wholesome Publisher
1231 S. Parker Rd. # 102
Denver, CO 80231
303-754-7095
SharoSward@aol.com
http://bookzone.com/bookzone/10000520.html